THE MONKEY'S PAW

W. W. Jacobs

retold by Hannah Fish

2

StandFor
graded readers

© 2016 – StandFor

Editorial Director	Lauri Cericato
Editorial Manager	Cayube Galas
Editorial Coordinator	Ana Carolina Costa Lopes
Series Editor	Nick Bullard
Editorial Assistant	Nathalia Thomaz
Production Manager	Mariana Milani
Production Coordinator	Marcelo Henrique Ferreira Fontes
Proofreader	Nicole Irving
Art Manager	Ricardo Borges
Art Coordinator	Daniela Di Creddo Máximo
Design	Yan Comunicação
Cover Design	Yan Comunicação
Art Supervisor	Patrícia De Michelis
Art Editors/Layout	Yan Comunicação, Lidiani Minoda
Illustrations Coordinator	Márcia Berne
Illustrations	Ulisses Figueiredo
Operations Director and Print Production Manager	Reginaldo Soares Damasceno

Dados Internacionais de Catalogação na Publicação (CIP)
(Câmara Brasileira do Livro, SP, Brasil)

Fish, Hannah
    The monkey's paw : standfor graded readers, level 2 / W. W. Jacobs ; retold by Hannah Fish ; Illustrated by Ulisses Figueiredo. -- 1. ed. -- São Paulo : FTD, 2016.

    ISBN 978-85-96-00431-2 (aluno)
    ISBN 978-85-96-00712-2 (professor)

    1. Literatura infantojuvenil I. Jacobs, W. W., 1863-1943. II. Figueiredo, Ulisses. III. Título.

16-04218   CDD-028.5

Índices para catálogo sistemático:

1. Literatura infantil   028.5
2. Literatura infantojuvenil   028.5

All rights reserved. No part of this publication may be reproduced, stored in a retrieval system, or transmitted, in any form or by any means, electronic, mechanical, photocopying, recording, or otherwise, without the prior written permission of StandFor.

This book is sold subject to the condition that it shall not, by way of trade or otherwise, be lent, resold, hired out, or otherwise circulated without the publisher's prior consent in any form of binding or cover than that in which it is published and without a similar condition being imposed on the subsequent purchaser.

Rua Rui Barbosa, 156 – Bela Vista – São Paulo-SP – Brasil – CEP 01326-010
Phone 0800 772 2300 – Caixa Postal 65149 – CEP 01390-970 – www.standfor.com.br

Impressão e Acabamento
Oceano Indústria Gráfica e Editora Ltda
Rua Osasco, 644 - Rod. Anhanguera, Km 33
CEP 07753-040 - Cajamar - SP
CNPJ: 67.795.906/0001-10

1 2 3 4 5 6 7 8 9

A - 613.142/20

THE MONKEY'S PAW

W. W. Jacobs was born in London in 1863. He studied at the University of London and then worked for the Post Office as a young man. He became a full-time writer in 1899. He is well-known for his short stories, many of which are humorous, although some are ghost stories. "The Monkey's Paw" was first published in 1902 and it is probably the most famous of all his stories. Jacobs died in London in 1943.

BEFORE READING

1 Match the names of the people in the story with their faces.

1. Mr. White

2. Mrs. White

3. Herbert White

4. Sergeant Morris

2 Match the words with their definitions.

1. monkey
2. paw
3. wish
4. magic
5. sergeant

a. the foot of an animal

b. an officer in the army

c. a type of animal that has a long tail and often lives in trees

d. something you want to happen

e. a power that can make impossible things happen

The Monkey's Paw

Outside the wind is blowing, and the cold rain is coming down onto a quiet and empty road. But inside the living room of a small house, a bright fire is keeping a family warm.

Old Mr. White is playing a game with his son, Herbert, and Mrs. White is sitting by the fire with her book. She has one eye on her book, and one eye on the game between father and son. Herbert is a smart young man and good at games, but old Mr. White doesn't like to lose!

The Monkey's Paw

"I win!" calls Herbert happily, as Mr. White hits his hand down on the table and stands up.

"Where is he?" the old man says angrily, and walks over to his wife and the warm fire. Mrs. White smiles at her son, but says nothing.

"It is cold and dark out there now," she says quietly to her husband, and nods to the window. "And look at that rain. The road is like a river. He can't come on a night like this."

But suddenly there is a knock at the door and Mr. White looks up in surprise.

The old man opens the door. There is a man outside in the rain, and Mr. White smiles at him warmly. The man is old too, but with dark hair. He comes into the house and takes off his wet hat and coat.

As they walk into the warm sitting room, Mr. White calls to his wife and his son, "This is Sergeant Morris. Back from India with stories to tell!"

Mrs. White and Herbert smile at the stranger in their living room, and Mrs. White gives the man her chair by the fire. Sergeant Morris sits down and Mrs. White goes to the kitchen to make him a drink.

With a glass in his hand, Morris begins to relax and he tells the family about his interesting travels around the world. He tells them of wonderful cities, colors, and food. He talks of strange people and unusual animals, and the family listens with excitement in their eyes.

Mr. White and Herbert have many questions for the sergeant, and he answers them happily. "I want to go to India one day," Mr. White tells his wife. She smiles at him and looks lovingly at his bright eyes.

"Tell us about the monkey's paw," Mr. White says with sudden excitement. Morris stops smiling and looks up at the old man. "Oh, no," he says darkly, "it is a bad thing, that paw. It is nothing for you good people to worry about."

"Go on!" Mr. White says brightly, and with a smile. He looks at his son and nods. "Herbert wants to know, don't you, Herbert?" he says with a laugh.

"Oh, well, it is a bit of magic, that is all," says Morris quietly. He puts his hand in his pocket and pulls out a small, black monkey's paw.

Mrs. White makes a small noise as she looks at the dirty little paw, but Herbert puts out his hand with interest. He takes the paw and looks at it carefully. "What is special about it, then?" he asks Morris.

"I have a good friend in India," Morris begins. "My friend knows a holy man and the paw is a gift from this special, magic man. The paw can give three wishes to three different men, and it's my paw now." Herbert makes an excited noise and starts to say something, but Morris quickly goes on. "But the wishes do not bring happiness," he says in a dark voice. "Only bad things come from the wishes."

"So why don't you have your wishes?" Herbert asks the sergeant quickly.

"I have," Morris answers quietly.

"And do you have what you want?" old Mrs. White now asks with interest.

"Well…" Morris begins, but Mr. White is excited and suddenly starts to speak.

"And what about the man before you – your friend?" he says.

"I don't know about his first two wishes, but his third wish was a wish to die. This paw is a gift from a dead man."

The Monkey's Paw

With these words, Morris throws the small black paw into the fire. Mrs. White calls out in surprise and Mr. White moves quickly and takes the monkey's paw from the fire.

"So now you don't need the paw," Mr. White says. "Why don't you give it to a third man? Why don't you give it to me?"

"That paw brings nothing but worry. Nothing but unhappiness!" Morris says in a sad voice. "Be a smart man and put it back on the fire."

"No, I want to keep it!" Mr. White says loudly, and the sergeant looks at him with worried eyes and shakes his head sadly.

"So how do you do it?" Mr. White asks his old friend. "How do you make a wish?"

"You take the paw in your right hand, and then you say your wish out loud." Morris begins. "But don't do it, I say. Don't make a wish! Don't you have all you need? Remember what I say. These wishes bring nothing but worry!"

Mrs. White looks at her husband and the sergeant and laughs quietly. "I don't know about magic," she says with a smile. "It sounds like a wonderful story to me!" Herbert begins to laugh, too. "How about wishing for four hands for me?" she says with a little laugh. "Then I can make dinner more quickly!"

Old Mr. White takes the paw in his right hand. With surprise in his eyes, Morris takes Mr. White by the arm and the old man, his wife, and his son laugh out loud.

But Morris does not laugh, and his eyes are dark as he says again to his friend, "Be a smart man and put the paw on the fire!"

But Mr. White puts the monkey's paw in his pocket and Mrs. White goes back into the kitchen to cook dinner. The three men sit around the table and talk about this and that.

At dinner, Morris tells the family more about his travels around the world and his years in India. They listen with interest and the room is full of happiness and laughter. The family forgets about the paw and the stories of magic and wishes.

It soon gets late and it is time for Morris to leave. He puts on his hat and his coat, and gives a nod of thanks to his old friend as the door closes behind him.

The Monkey's Paw

"Did you give him anything for the paw?" Mrs. White asks her husband after Morris leaves.

"Just a little money," the old man says. "He didn't want it, but I gave it to him all the same."

Herbert laughs happily and says, "We can be rich now, father! Rich and happy! For your first wish, wish for lots of money!"

Mr. White takes the monkey's paw from his pocket. Mrs. White again makes a small noise as she looks at the paw. "It's so old and dirty," she says. "I don't like to look at it!"

"Go on, Father, make a wish!" Herbert says with excitement in his voice.

"But what do I need?" says the old man to his son. "I have all I need here in this house."

"Wish for more money then," Herbert says. "We can always have more money."

So Mr. White takes the small paw in his right hand and says out loud, "I wish for two hundred pounds."

Suddenly the old man cries out. Mrs. White quickly runs to him with a worried look on her face.

"It's moving!" he shouts. "The paw is moving in my hand!" He quickly throws the paw to the floor.

Mr. White stands with his mouth open, looking at the paw on the living room floor.

"Well, I don't see any money," Herbert says, and he picks up the paw and puts it on the table.

Mrs. White takes her husband's arm, "Don't worry, all is well. Come and sit down by the fire and get warm. You are as white as snow."

The family sits together by the fire, and soon it is time for bed. Herbert goes up first, and then his mother. Old Mr. White sits for some time and thinks about his old friend Sergeant Morris. He looks into the fire and sees strange pictures. He sees animals dancing.

He sees a monkey's face with bright red eyes. It is time for bed. He slowly gets up out of the chair and with a last look at the paw on the table, goes upstairs to bed.

The next morning is bright. There is no more rain and the sun is in the sky. Mr. White feels happy as he looks at his wife and his son. They are sitting at the breakfast table and Herbert looks up and smiles at his father. Mrs. White nods at her husband to sit down for breakfast. "Your friend Morris tells some wonderful stories!" she says to him. "There can't be magic now!"

"Yes, and how can two hundred pounds hurt you?" says Herbert with a laugh.

Old Mr. White looks at them and smiles. The monkey's paw is now in a drawer and he feels happy about that!

Herbert finishes his breakfast and gets up to go to work. Soon he says goodbye to his mother and father and closes the door behind him.

Mrs. White looks out the window and watches Herbert walk up the road. Then she sits at the table and smiles at her husband. She feels happy, too. The monkey's paw is a good story. Sergeant Morris likes to surprise people by telling them interesting stories about India.

But when the postman comes, Mrs. White quickly goes to have a look through the letters. She feels a little unhappy when she doesn't find two hundred pounds!

It is time for lunch and Mr. and Mrs. White sit down at the table again.

The Monkey's Paw

The sun is now high in the sky, and the room is bright. The husband and wife talk about this and that, and are happy. Then Mrs. White sees a stranger outside the house. She goes to the window and looks out. "Look at that man," she says to her husband. "He is standing right outside our house, but I don't know him. Do you?"

Mr. White walks over to his wife and looks out the window, too. "No, I don't know him," he tells her. The stranger is outside Mr. and Mrs. White's house for some time. He looks around unhappily, and walks up and down, up and down.

Then the man suddenly looks up, and Mr. and Mrs. White watch as he walks to their door.

Mrs. White goes to the door and opens it. The stranger looks at Mrs. White, but he doesn't smile. He is tall and has a good coat, good clothes, and good clean shoes. It makes Mrs. White think about the monkey's paw and the two hundred pounds. She takes the man into the living room to meet Mr. White.

Old Mr. White smiles at the stranger, but the man just looks at him and doesn't say anything. He has a worried look on his face.

The Monkey's Paw

After some time, the stranger speaks. "I come from Maw and Meggins," he says.

Mrs. White then quickly starts to speak. "Oh, that is where Herbert works. Is everything OK? Is he OK? What is it? What is it?"

"Don't worry," Mr. White says quietly to his wife. "I am sure Herbert is fine. Sit down and let the man speak."

"I am sorry," the man says in a quiet voice.

"Oh no!" Mrs. White calls out. "Is he OK? Where is he?"

The man from Maw and Meggins looks at the floor sadly. "I am sorry," he says again. Mr. and Mrs. White look at him with big eyes and worried faces. "Herbert works with a lot of machinery," the man goes on, "and this morning… Oh, it is bad. I am so sorry." The man looks up at the worried faces of Mr. and Mrs. White.

"Oh, is he in pain? Is he in pain? Please tell me where he is!" Mrs. White calls out.

"He isn't in pain now," the man says in a sad voice.

"Oh, good," Mrs. White begins to say, but then she understands what those words mean. She falls to the floor and cries out sadly, "No!"

Mr. White sits by his wife and takes her in his arms. She is crying and he takes her hand in his.

"He is our only son." Mr. White says to the stranger in their living room. "This is very hard for us."

The man looks at Mr. White sadly.

The Monkey's Paw

"Maw and Meggins are very sorry for you," he says quietly, "and they want to help you," he goes on. "I am here for them, and they want me to give you some money... to say sorry."

Mr. and Mrs. White look at the man. Old Mr. White lets his wife's hand fall from his and he stands up. His face is white and his mouth is open. "How much?" he says to the man quietly, his voice now shaking.

The man looks at Mr. White. "Two hundred pounds," he says.

Mr. White suddenly feels sick. He makes a small noise and falls to the floor.

Mr. and Mrs. White go to church and say goodbye to Herbert. It feels so wrong to say goodbye to their son. They see friends at the church, but they cannot speak to them. They are too tired – too sad.

It is all over very quickly, and soon Mr. and Mrs. White are in their house again. But how can they live in the house without Herbert? Mrs. White wants something to happen. Something to take her pain away. Something to make things better. But nothing happens. Nothing changes – Herbert is not there.

The house is quiet now that Herbert and his laughter are not there. Mr. and Mrs. White never smile or laugh, and they cannot sleep, so they are exhausted. The old man and woman sit at their table and they look out the window, but they say very little. They have nothing to say. The house feels empty without Herbert in it. Their days are quiet and they pass slowly.

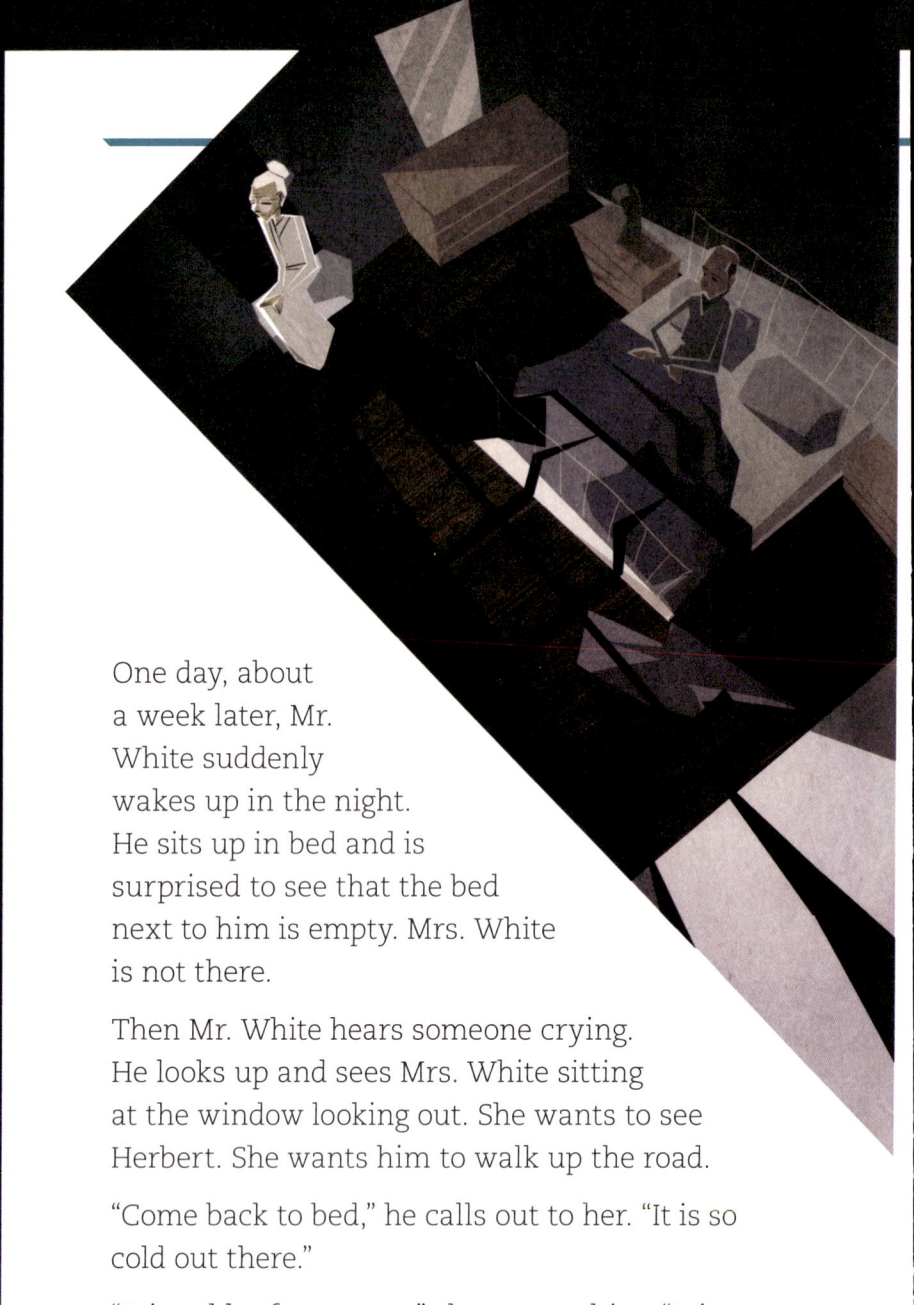

One day, about a week later, Mr. White suddenly wakes up in the night. He sits up in bed and is surprised to see that the bed next to him is empty. Mrs. White is not there.

Then Mr. White hears someone crying. He looks up and sees Mrs. White sitting at the window looking out. She wants to see Herbert. She wants him to walk up the road.

"Come back to bed," he calls out to her. "It is so cold out there."

"It is colder for my son," she says to him. "It is colder for poor Herbert." Mrs. White cries as she looks out the window.

It is warm in the bed and Mr. White's eyes start to close again. But then he wakes suddenly to a loud call from his wife. "The paw," she cries out loudly. "The monkey's paw!"

The old man sits up in bed quickly. "What? Where? Where is it?" he asks his wife.

Mrs. White leaves the window and comes across the room to the bed and to her husband. "The monkey's paw," she says again in an excited voice. "Do we have it? Do we have it?"

"Yes, yes, we have it. It is downstairs," the old man says in a surprised voice. "Why?"

The Monkey's Paw

Mrs. White is laughing now. She is crying and laughing at the same time. She looks at her husband and her eyes are big and bright.

Mr. White feels scared. "What is it?" he says to her in a loud voice.

"The paw. Where is it? Where is the monkey's paw?" she asks him quickly.

"It is downstairs," the old man tells his wife again. "I put it in a drawer in the living room."

Mrs. White makes a happy noise and laughs again.

"What is it? Tell me! What do you want with the monkey's paw?" Mr. White asks his wife.

She looks at him with bright eyes and laughs. "The wishes," she says in a happy voice. "The wishes! We have two more wishes. The monkey's paw gives three wishes!"

"What!" Mr. White cries out and he quickly gets out of bed. "Are you crazy? One wish is too many! Remember! We don't want more wishes!"

But Mrs. White's eyes are crazy and she isn't listening to her husband. "Oh, yes we do," she says loudly. "We want one more wish. We can wish for Herbert! We can wish for him to come back to us!" she says in a happy voice.

Oh no, you *are* crazy!" Mr. White cries out. "You don't know what you are saying. Go back to bed. Please go back to bed."

But Mrs. White stops laughing and looks at her husband with dark eyes. "Go and get the paw," she says in a loud voice.

"It is ten days now," Mr. White cries at his wife. "Herbert is dead for ten days! Think about it!"

"Are you scared of your son? Are you scared of Herbert?" Mrs. White asks angrily. "Now go and get the paw!"

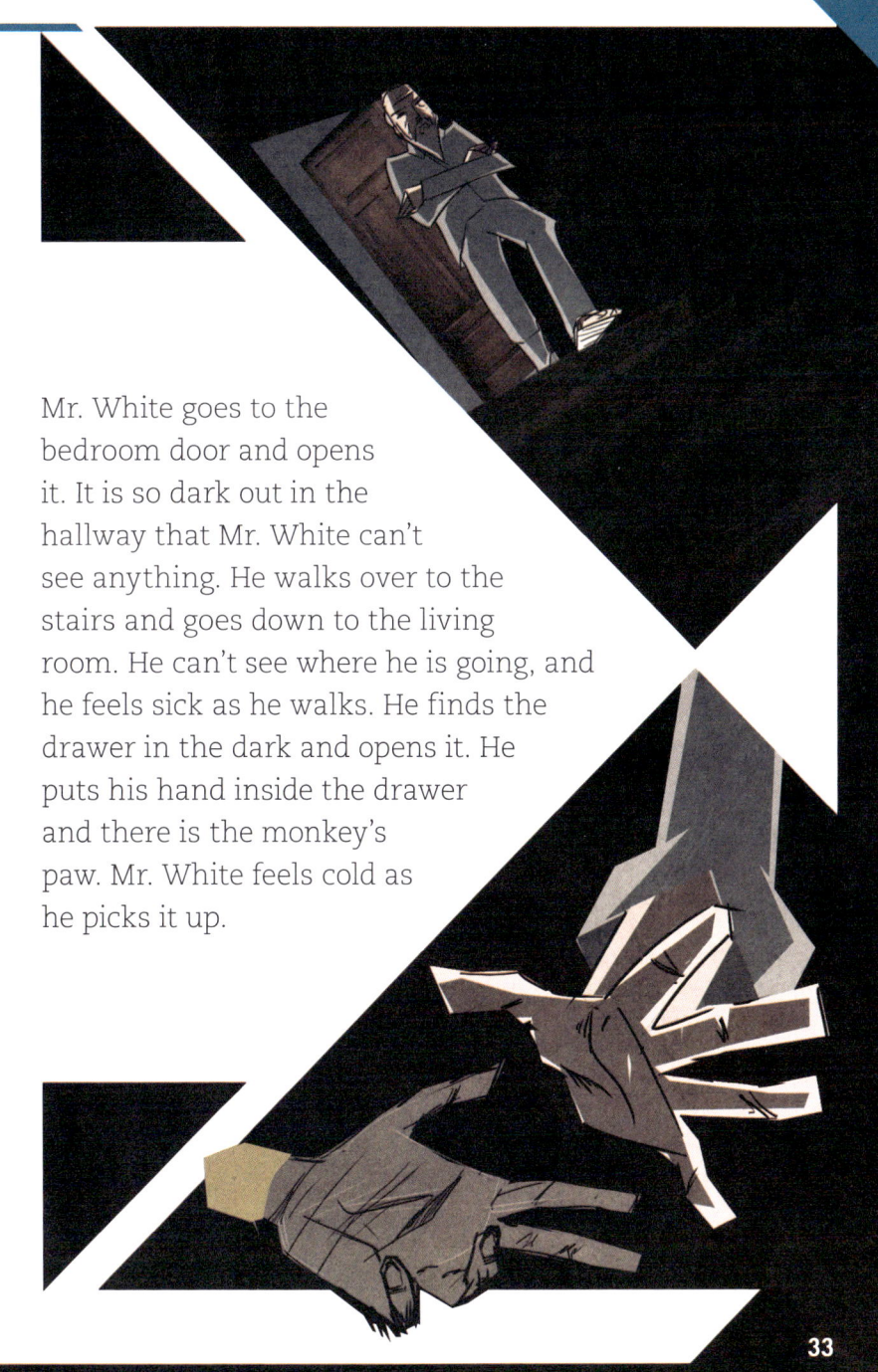

Mr. White goes to the bedroom door and opens it. It is so dark out in the hallway that Mr. White can't see anything. He walks over to the stairs and goes down to the living room. He can't see where he is going, and he feels sick as he walks. He finds the drawer in the dark and opens it. He puts his hand inside the drawer and there is the monkey's paw. Mr. White feels cold as he picks it up.

With the monkey's paw in his hand, Mr. White moves back to the living room door. But in the dark he can't find the door. He feels so scared, it is hard for him to move. "Herbert is dead ten days," he thinks as he walks. "His face. The machinery. Oh, he can't come back."

At last he finds the stairs and goes up to find his wife. As he walks into the bedroom Mrs. White is waiting for him.

"Do you have it?" she asks in an excited voice. Mr. White looks at his wife's face and he doesn't know it. It looks crazy to him.

"We can't do this," he says to her quietly.

"Wish," she says in a strange voice.

"It is wrong!" he says, more loudly than before.

But now Mrs. White shouts, "Wish!"

The Monkey's Paw

So Mr. White takes the monkey's paw in his right hand and says, "I wish for Herbert to come back to us," and then he throws the paw to the floor. He looks at the paw with scared eyes and falls on to the bed.

Mrs. White says nothing, but has a strange smile on her face. She walks to the window and looks out. Mr. White sits on the bed for a long time and watches his wife. She sits at the window. She doesn't speak or move. She just sits and looks out onto the empty road – and waits for Herbert.

After a long time, Mr. and Mrs. White get into bed. It is very late, and the room is now freezing cold. The old man is in bed next to his wife, but they do not speak.

The Monkey's Paw

Mr. White cannot sleep. After some time, he gets up and in the dark room he finds the door. He goes out into the hallway, down the stairs, and starts to go into the living room.

At the living room door he stops, and then he hears it – a quiet knock on the door. The knock is so quiet, it is difficult to hear. The color goes from Mr. White's face and he suddenly feels sick.

He quickly goes back to the stairs and starts to go up. He stops on the stairs as he hears a second knock. His hands and legs are shaking now.

As quickly as he can, he runs up the stairs and into the bedroom. He closes the door behind him to stop the noise, and gets back into bed.

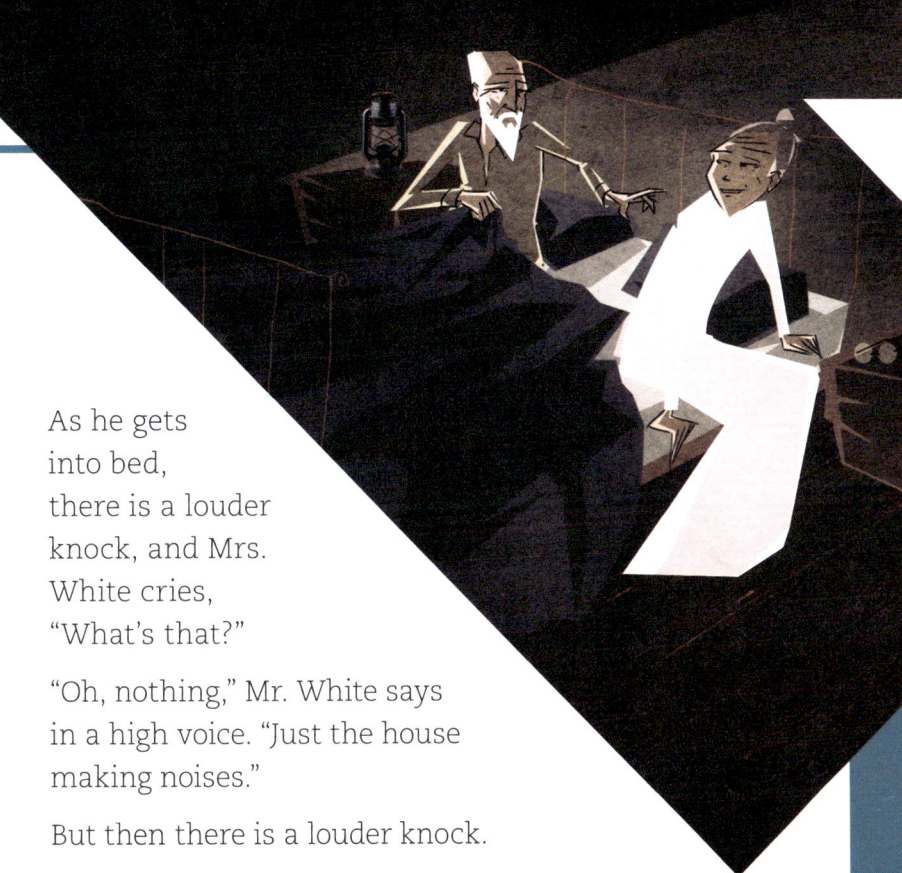

As he gets
into bed,
there is a louder
knock, and Mrs.
White cries,
"What's that?"

"Oh, nothing," Mr. White says
in a high voice. "Just the house
making noises."

But then there is a louder knock.

"It's him. It's Herbert!" Mrs. White calls out excitedly. "It's Herbert. He is here. He is back!" she cries as she gets out of bed. She looks at her husband and laughs. "Go and open the door!" she tells him, but Mr. White does not move.

"No!" he cries to his wife. He takes her hand and looks at her with scared eyes. "We can't. We can't! Don't do it – don't open the door!"

"You are scared of our son!" she cries at him. "Let me go!"

"Please, don't do it," he says to her again. "Please don't open the door."

But Mrs. White isn't listening to her husband, and she runs out of the bedroom. There is a loud knock on the door.

"Don't open that door!" he calls after her. But she is running down the stairs. Suddenly Mr. White thinks about the monkey's paw. "The third wish," he thinks. "There is one more wish."

Mr. White quickly looks on the bedroom floor, but he can't see the paw. He can hear Mrs. White running down the stairs, and the knocks are getting louder and louder.

Mrs. White is down the stairs now and very close to the door. She cries out, "I'm coming, Herbert! I'm coming!"

Then suddenly Mr. White sees the paw under the bed. He falls to the floor to get it. He can hear Mrs. White at the door. The knocks are so loud now that it is difficult to think.

The Monkey's Paw

Mr. White takes the paw in his right hand and he quickly says his third wish.

At the same time, Mrs. White throws open the door. A cold wind comes blowing into the house, and Mrs. White cries out in sadness.

Mr. White runs down the stairs to his wife. She is now sitting by the door with her head down. He can hear her crying. The door is open, and with shaking legs, Mr. White goes over to it and looks out onto a quiet and empty road.

WHILE READING ACTIVITIES

Read pages 5 to 8.

1 Are these sentences true or false?

1. It is a cold night, and it is snowing. `F`
2. Mr. White and Herbert are playing a game. ☐
3. Mrs. White is sitting at the table with a cup of tea. ☐
4. Suddenly there is a knock at the door. ☐
5. There is a young woman at the door. ☐
6. Sergeant Morris is an old friend of Mr. White. ☐
7. Sergeant Morris tells the family about his travels. ☐
8. Mr. White wants to go to India. ☐

Read pages 9 to 13.

2 Who says this? Write the names.

1. "Be a smart man and put it back on the fire." _Sergeant Morris_
2. "So why don't you have your wishes?" _____
3. "This paw is a gift from a dead man." _____
4. "And do you have what you want?" _____
5. "How do you make a wish?" _____
6. "It is a bad thing, that paw." _____
7. "Tell us about the monkey's paw." _____
8. "You take the paw in your right hand, and then you say your wish out loud." _____
9. "Why don't you give it to me?" _____
10. "These wishes bring nothing but worry!" _____

3 Answer the questions.

1. Who has the monkey's paw? _Sergeant Morris_
2. Does Sergeant Morris think the paw is good or bad? _____
3. Which country does the paw come from? _____
4. What sort of man does the paw come from? _____

5. How many men can have the wishes? _____
6. How many wishes can each man have? _____
7. What does Sergeant Morris do with the paw?

   _____

8. Who takes the paw from the fire? _____
9. How do you make a wish?

   _____

10. What does Sergeant Morris say the wishes bring?

    _____

Read pages 14 to 18.

4 Complete the sentences with a word from the box.

> pocket two hundred bed hands coat
> fire paw money pictures India dirty

1. Mrs. White says to wish for four ___hands___ for her.
2. Sergeant Morris wants Mr. White to put the paw on the _____.
3. Mr. White puts the paw in his _____.
4. At dinner, Morris tells the family a lot of stories about his time in _____.
5. Sergeant Morris puts on his hat and _____ and leaves.
6. Mr. White gives Morris a little _____ for the paw.
7. The paw is old and _____.
8. Mr. White wishes for _____ pounds.
9. When Mr. White takes it from his pocket and makes the wish, the _____ moves in his hand.
10. Herbert and Mrs. White go up to _____.
11. Mr. White sees strange _____ in the fire.

WHILE READING ACTIVITIES

Read pages 19 to 25.

5 Put the sentences in the correct order. Number them 1 through 10.

a. Mr. and Mrs. White sit at the table for lunch. ☐

b. Mrs. White opens the door and takes the man into the living room. ☐

c. Mrs. White looks through the letters from the postman. ☐

d. The man gives Mr. and Mrs. White two hundred pounds. ☐

e. Mr. and Mrs. White and Herbert have breakfast. ☐1

f. Mrs. White sees a strange man outside their house. ☐

g. The man tells Mr. and Mrs. White that he is from Maw and Meggins, where Herbert works. ☐

h. Herbert goes off to work. ☐

i. The man tells Mr. and Mrs. White that Herbert is dead. ☐

j. The stranger knocks on Mr. and Mrs. White's door. ☐

Read pages 26 to 29.

6 Answer the questions.

1. Where do Mr. and Mrs. White say goodbye to Herbert?
   at church

2. Why don't Mr. and Mrs. White speak to their friends?
   _____

3. How does the house feel without Herbert?
   _____

4. How do Mr. and Mrs. White feel without Herbert?
   _____

5. Where is Mrs. White when Mr. White wakes up?
   _____

6. Why is Mrs. White crying?
   _____

7. What does Mrs. White suddenly shout for?

_____

8. Why do you think Mrs. White wants the monkey's paw?

_____

Read pages 30 to 39

7 Circle the correct words to complete the sentences.

1. The monkey's paw is in a drawer in the (living room) / kitchen.

2. Mrs. White is crying and *laughing / singing* at the same time.

3. Mrs. White wants Mr. White to get *Herbert / the monkey's paw*.

4. Mrs. White *doesn't want / wants* to have one more wish.

5. Mr. White thinks the wish is a *good / bad* idea.

6. Mr. White goes to the living room to get *the paw / a drink*.

7. *Mr. / Mrs.* White wishes for Herbert to come back.

8. Mr. White can't *sleep / wait*, so he gets up.

9. Mr. White hears *rain outside / a knock* at the door.

10. When he hears the knock, Mr. White feels *happy / sick*.

8 Answer the questions.

1. Why is Mrs. White so happy and excited?

2. Why does Mr. White think the wish is a bad idea?

3. Who do you think is at the door?

4. What is Mr. White's third wish?

5. How do you think Mr. and Mrs. White's lives are for the next few years?

AFTER READING ACTIVITIES

1 Put the sentences in the correct order. Number them 1 through 14.

a. Sergeant Morris shows the family a monkey's paw. ☐

b. Mr. White wishes for two hundred pounds. ☐

c. Mr. White and Herbert are at the table playing a game and Mrs. White is watching them. [1]

d. Mr. White wakes up one night and Mrs. White is at the bedroom window. ☐

e. The man tells them that Herbert is dead and gives them two hundred pounds. ☐

f. In the middle of the night Mr. White hears a knock at the door. ☐

g. Mr. White gets the paw and wishes for Herbert to come back. ☐

h. The family has breakfast and Herbert goes to work. ☐

i. Mrs. White tells Mr. White to get the monkey's paw and make a wish. ☐

j. Morris throws the monkey's paw in the fire, but Mr. White takes it out. ☐

k. Mr. and Mrs. White go to church to say goodbye to Herbert. ☐

l. A man from Maw and Meggins comes to see Mr. and Mrs. White. ☐

m. Mr. White makes a third wish, and Mrs. White opens the door onto an empty road. ☐

n. There is a knock at the door and it is Mr. White's old friend Sergeant Morris. ☐

2 What do you think about Mr. and Mrs. White? Write about them.

3 Look at the pictures and answer the questions.

1. What is Mrs. White thinking in this picture?

2. Where is Mr. White? What is he thinking?

3. What does Mr. White say when he picks up the monkey's paw?

GLOSSARY

blow when air moves, it blows

bright with a lot of light

crazy stupid, not sensible

drawer a wooden box that you can pull out of furniture

empty with nothing inside

hallway the first room you come to in a house

holy connected with religion

knock the noise when someone hits a door because they want to come in

laughter the noise you make when you are very happy or amused

loud with a lot of noise; not quiet

machinery things with moving parts

magic something that happens by special powers

monkey an animal with a long tail which often lives in trees

nod move your head up and down, to say "yes"

pain the feeling when you are hurt

paw the foot of an animal

pick up take in your hand

postman the person who brings letters (post) to your house

rich with a lot of money

sad not happy

scared frightened of danger

sergeant a person in the army

shake move from side to side

smart intelligent and able to think quickly

stairs the things you go up to go to the upper part of a house

stranger a person you do not know

surprise something that you don't expect

throw make something move out of your hand

voice you speak with your voice

wake up when you finish sleeping, you wake up

warm a little hot

win to come first in a game

wind air that moves

wish something that you want to happen

StandFor Readers

StandFor Readers provide a range of extensive reading materials for learners of all ages. The readers are carefully selected to cater for a range of interests, and are available across nine levels. Each title is meticulously graded for both vocabulary and structure, and topics have been selected to reflect the age and ability of students. Standfor Graded Readers are graded according to the Common European Framework of Reference for Languages (CEFR). Factual titles respond to the need for Content and Language Integrated Learning materials.

StandFor Young Readers

Level 1 — 125 Headwords
- The Enormous Turnip
- Little Red Hen
- The Three Little Pigs
- Katie's Camera

Level 2 — 240 Headwords
- The Cats and the Fishes
- The Gingerbread Man
- The Three Hungry Goats
- Peach Boy

Level 3 — 390 Headwords
- The Emperor's New Clothes
- The Little Prince
- Little Red Riding Hood
- The Town Mouse and the Country Mouse
- What Is Inside the Big Red Suitcase?

Level 4 — 540 Headwords
- Arachne
- Couscous
- Puss in Boots
- Transportation Around the World
- The Twelve Months

Level 5 — 680 Headwords
- Dragon Boat
- Icarus
- Let's Go to the City
- Nuala
- The Stories of King Arthur

StandFor Graded Readers

Level 1 — 380 Headwords — CEFR: A1
- The Adventures of Tom Sawyer
- Festivals
- Rip Van Winkle

Level 2 — 580 Headwords — CEFR: A2
- Great Navigators
- The Monkey's Paw
- Sherlock Holmes: The Yellow Band

Level 3 — 800 Headwords — CEFR: A2
- The Black Cat and Other Stories
- Oceans
- The Ransom of Red Chief and Other Stories

Level 4 — 1000 Headwords — CEFR: B1
- The Call of the Wild
- Climate Change
- Robinson Crusoe